This copy of
THE FUNNIEST
JOKE BOOK
Compiled by
JIM ELDRIDGE
belongs to

. . . .

THE FUNNIEST JOKE BOOK

COMPILED BY
JIM ELDRIDGE

ILLUSTRATED BY
COLIN WEST

SPARROW
BOOKS

A Sparrow Book
Published by Arrow Books Limited
17-21 Conway Street, London W1P 6JD

An imprint of the Hutchinson Publishing Group

London Melbourne Sydney Auckland
Johannesburg and agencies throughout
the world

First published 1983

Set in Linotron Century by
Book Economy Services, Crawley, Sussex.

Made and printed in Great Britain
by The Anchor Press Ltd
Tiptree, Essex

ISBN 0 09 931330 8

With special thanks for all their help to Steve
Stone, Professor Bullseye, and all the staff at the
Luton Leader; Jeremy Smith at the *Evening
Post-Echo*; and all the staff at the children's
libraries in Luton, Dunstable, and Leighton
Buzzard; and the staff and children of the Junior
Schools – especially Denbigh Junior School,
Luton – who all became my central clearing
houses for the deluge of hundreds of jokes, and
without whom this book would never have
happened.

Jim Eldridge

What's the fastest way to catch a squirrel?
Hang from a branch and act like a nut.

How do you stop a bull from charging?
Take away its credit card.

Why does Batman carry worms?
To feed Robin.

There were two octopuses, and one octopus said to the other octopus: 'Let me hold your hand, your hand, your hand, your hand, your hand, your hand, your hand.'

Angry man: I'll teach you to throw stones at my greenhouse!
Boy: *I wish you would, I've thrown ten stones and only hit it twice.*

First rabbit: I bought a gold watch yesterday.
Second rabbit: Was it very expensive?
First rabbit: Yes, 25 carrots.

There were three tomatoes walking along the road: a Mummy and Daddy in front and a baby at the back who couldn't go very fast. So the Daddy one went back to the baby and stamped on it and squashed it, and said, 'Come on now, catch up!' (Ketchup)

I know a joke about butter, but I better not tell you or you might spread it.

Why did the tonsils get dressed?
The doctor was taking them out.

What has two handles and flies?
A dustbin.

A man wanted to buy a Rolls Royce, but he was 2p short of £9,998. He stopped a man outside the car shop and asked him for 2p to buy a Rolls Royce, and the man said, 'Here's 4p – buy one for me as well.'

What do you get if you drop a piano down a mine?
A flat miner.

Teacher (on telephone): So you say John is too ill to come to school?
Voice at other end: That's right.
Teacher: Who am I talking to?
Voice at the other end: This is my father.

It's raining cats and dogs.
I know, I've just stepped in a poodle.

Why do witches ride on broomsticks?
Because vacuum clean-ers are too heavy.

Why did the little girl tiptoe past the medicine cabinet?
She didn't want to wake the sleeping pills.

What's Father Christmas's wife's name?
Mary Christmas.

Why do cows wear bells?
Because their horns don't work.

Why did the man take the pencil to bed?
He wanted to draw the curtains.

When is it bad luck to have a cat on your path?
When you are a mouse.

What is an octopus?
An eight-sided cat.

How do you stop a cockerel crowing in the morning?
Eat it the night before.

What did the traffic light say to the car?
Don't look, I'm changing.

Mum, I don't like cheese with holes.
Well, eat the cheese and leave the holes.

Woman: I think it's most unfair for this man to charge us £20 for towing us two miles.
Man: *That's all right, he's earning it. I've got the brakes on.*

When is a bone a musical instrument?
When it's a trombone.

What is full of holes but can hold water?
A sponge.

What did the biscuit say when run over by a bus?
Oh crumbs!

What did the big telephone say to the little telephone?
You're too young to be engaged.

A man walking in the countryside noticed a horse in a field, and as he passed the horse it said: 'I won a Grand National eight years ago.' The man was so surprised he went to the farmer and told him what had happened. The farmer said, 'That's not true, he only came second.'

What do you put in an apple pie?
Your teeth.

I have a black and white dog because the licence is cheaper.

How do you keep an idiot in suspense?
I'll tell you tomorrow.

What's big and red and lies on the ground?
A dead bus.

Why are elephants crinkled?
Have you ever tried to iron one?

I'd tell you the joke about the broken pencil, but there's no point to it.

Who took Little Bo Peep's sheep? I reckon it was that crook she had with her.

Why do birds fly south in winter?
It's too far to walk.

I think my bucket's ill.
Why?
It's a little pail.

My friend always wears sunglasses. He takes a dim view of things.

Customer: Do you have any invisible ink?
Shopkeeper: Yes, sir. What colour would you like?

A man went into a shop and asked for 20 moth balls. The next day he went in and asked for 50 moth balls. When he went in for a third time and asked for another 50, the shopkeeper asked him why he bought so many, and the man replied, 'Every time I throw them, I miss.'

Who is the biggest: Mr Bigger, Mrs Bigger, or Baby Bigger?
Baby Bigger, because he is just a little Bigger.

What pine has the sharpest needles?
A porcupine.

What goes 'oom oom'?
A cow walking backwards.

What nut is like a sneeze?
A cashew nut.

Girl: Would you tell me off for something I didn't do?
Teacher: No, why?
Girl: Good, because I haven't done my homework.

What is yellow and dangerous?
A banana with a machine gun.

A dog was sitting by the fire chewing a bone. When he got up he only had three legs.

What did the littlest apple say to the biggest apple?
Core!

What begins with T, ends with T, and has T in it?
Teapot.

What train carries bubble gum?
A chew chew train.

What steps should be taken if a lion charges?
Long ones.

What did the candle say to the other candle?
Are you going out tonight?

What do ghosts eat for supper?
Spook-etti.

If you sleep like a log in the night, where do you find yourself in the morning?
In the fireplace.

A man was spreading elephant poison all over the road when a policeman came along and said, 'What are you doing?' 'Spreading elephant poison to get rid of the elephants,' said the man. 'But there aren't any elephants around here,' pointed out the policeman. 'I know,' said the man. 'It's working well, isn't it?'

Why did the tomato blush?
Because it saw the salad dressing.

Why do bakers always want dough?
Because they knead it.

Quick, Mum, I've knocked over the ladder at the side of the house!
I'm busy, go and tell your father.
He knows, he's hanging from the roof.

What exams do horses take?
Hay levels.

There were three cows in a meadow, one was called Daisy, one was called Sally, and one was called What. Sally and Daisy went for a walk, who was left?
What.
There were three cows in a meadow. . . .

Why haven't you opened the piano?
The keys are inside.

I couldn't afford a parrot so I bought a bird that was going cheep.

Dad: Sally, shouldn't you give the goldfish some fresh water?
Sally: No, they haven't drunk the last lot yet.

What are the fastest vegetables?
Runner beans.

What do you give a hurt lemon?
Lemon-ade.

Son: Dad, I took all the television apart and put it back together again.
Dad: I hope you haven't lost any bits.
Son: No, but I've got 15 bits left over.

What did one magnet say to the other?
My, you are attractive.

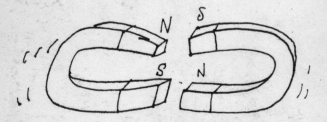

What shoes are made of banana skins?
Slippers.

Why did the man put dirt in his shoes?
He wanted his corn to grow.

On which side do chickens have the most feathers?
The outside.

What happened to the two kangaroos who got married?
They lived hoppily ever after.

Mother: Jimmy, you mustn't fight. I've told you, you should learn to give and take.
Jimmy: I did, I gave him a black eye and took his orange.

A man was in front of a firing squad and was asked if he had a last request before he was shot. 'Yes,' he said, 'I'd like to sing a song.' 'Certainly,' said the leader of the firing squad, 'go ahead.' The man started to sing: '10,000 green apples hanging on the wall. . . .'

Army recruit: What happens if this parachute fails to open?
Army instructor: Bring it back and we'll give you another.

First dog: My name's Fido. What's yours?
Second dog: I'm not sure but I think it's Down Boy.

Why do elephants have big ears?
Because Noddy wouldn't pay the ransom.

What has one horn and gives milk?
A milk truck.

Boy: When I grow up I'm going to be a policeman and follow in my father's footsteps.
Friend: I didn't know your dad was a policeman.
Boy: He isn't, he's a burglar.

Child: Help! I can't swim!
Lifeguard: Why not?
Child: The tide's out.

What did the grape say to the other grape?
Nothing, grapes can't talk.

Father: Well, John, do you think your teacher likes you?
John: Oh yes, she puts kisses by all the sums I do.

What is the best place to weigh whales?
At the whale-weigh station.

What's green and hairy and goes up and down?
A gooseberry in a lift.

Alice: Why do you call your husband Treasure?
Sally: Because people keep asking where I dug him up.

What happens if you dial 666?
A policeman comes standing on his head.

LOONY LIBRARY

A Quick Snack by *Roland Butter*.

Dangerous Pathway by *Hugo First*.

Jungle animals by *Ann T. Lope*.

Baby Sitting by *Justin Casey Howls*.

Bricks and Mortar by *Bill Ding*.

Explosives by *Dinah Mite*.

The Chinese Weekend by *Fri Sat Sun*.

Merry Christmas by *Miss L. Toe*.

Winter by *I.C. Days*.

Medical Cure by *Penny Sillin*.

The Hot Room by *Ray D. Ator*.

The Long Walk by *Miss D. Bus*.

Accident on the Cliff Top by *Eileen Dover*.

Rush to the Loo by *Willy Makit*.

Why I Stopped Running by *Ivor Blister*.

The Countryside in Spring by *Teresa Green*.

Keeping Rubbish In by *Lydia Dustbin*.

40 Days In The Saddle by *Major Bumsore*.

Punctured by *Buster Tyre*.

Smack by *Ben Dover*.

The Millionaire by *Ivor Fortune*.

Constant Complaining by *Mona Lott*.

My Feet Ache by *Carrie Mee*.

On the Beach by *C. Side*.

Get Rich Quick by *Robin Banks*.

THE DOG'S DINNER BY Norah Bone

GROWING RICE BY Paddy Fields

PANTS AROUND MY ANKLES BY Lucy Lastic

Customer: I'd like to buy that dog but his legs are too short.
Pet shop owner: Too short? They all touch the ground, don't they?

Harry: I know a man called Arthur Smells, and he wants to change his name.
Larry: I'm not surprised. What's he changing it to?
Harry: Fred Smells.

Did you hear about the plastic surgeon who fell asleep in front of the fire? He melted.

What happened to the snake that caught a cold?
She adder viper nose.

Why did the duck cross the road?
To prove he wasn't chicken.

Father: Why were you kept in after school, son?
Son: I didn't know where the Orkneys were, Dad.
Father: Well in future remember where you put things.

What did the budgie become when the lawn mower ran over it?
Shredded tweet.

Teacher: Name me a liquid that won't freeze.
Child: Hot water.

What is a myth?
A female moth.

What's black, white and red?
A sunburnt penguin.

Fred: I had to have my dog put down.
Joe: Was he mad?
Fred: Well, he wasn't pleased.

Why do elephants have fleas?
Because fleas can't have elephants.

Judge: Is this the first time you've been up before me?
Prisoner: I don't know, your honour, what time do you normally get up?

How many people work in your office?
About half of them.

Teacher: Stephen, where are you from?
Stephen: Scotland, sir.
Teacher: What part?
Stephen: All of me, sir.

What do you get when you pour boiling water down a rabbit hole?
Hot cross bunnies.

What do you give as a parting present?
A comb.

Why don't centipedes play football?
Because by the time they get their boots on the game will be over.

What's a cat's favourite holiday resort?
The Canary Islands.

If there's an umpire in cricket, a referee in football, what is there in bowls?
Goldfish.

What comes after Humphrey?
Humphour.

Where do farmers leave their pigs when they go to town?
At porking meters.

Gardener: I put manure on my rhubarb.
Child: I prefer custard on mine.

Why does the sea never sleep?
Because it has a rocky bed.

What's red and goes beep beep?
A strawberry in a traffic jam.

I had to give up tap
dancing as I kept falling
in the bath.

I thought you were supposed to come yesterday to mend the doorbell.
I did, madam. I rang twice but I got no answer.

What did the carpet say to the floor?
I've got you covered.

Why do they put telephone wires up so high?
To keep up the conversation.

What would you do with a sick wasp?
Take it to waspital.

What did the toothpaste say to the brush?
Give me a squeeze and I'll meet you outside the tube.

Why do dragons sleep in the daytime?
They like to hunt knights.

What's the difference between an injured lion and bad weather?
One roars with pain and the other pours with rain.

What do computers eat?
Fission chips.

In a railway carriage an old lady was annoyed by a little boy who kept sniffing. Finally she asked, 'Haven't you got a handkerchief?' 'Yes,' said the boy, 'but my Mum wouldn't like me to lend it to a stranger.'

A noise woke me up this morning.
What was it?
The crack of dawn.

A boy was caught scrumping up a tree by a farmer, who shouted up at him, 'Come down this minute or I'll tell your father!' 'You can tell him now,' said the boy, 'he's up here with me.'

My dog's got no nose.
How does it smell?
Terrible.

What man earns his living by driving his customers away?
A taxi driver.

How do you hire a horse?
Stand it on four bricks.

How do you make a swiss roll?
Push him down a hill.

What's a Grecian urn?
£2 pounds a week.

What is the largest mouse in the world?
A hippopotamouse.

A lorry carrying five tons of human hair crashed today. Police are combing the area.

What must a person be to receive a state funeral?
Dead.

The solicitor was reading Fred's will: 'I said I'd mention my brother in my will, so Hello, brother!'

The police are looking for a man with one eye. Why don't they use two?

What's the difference between a wizard and the letters KEMAS?
One makes spells and the others spell MAKES.

An Englishman on holiday in Texas was amazed how large everything was. The cars were as long as buses, the bedrooms as big as warehouses. One night he got drunk and fell into a swimming pool. When people rushed to rescue him, he yelled, 'Don't flush it, don't flush it!'

Why are you pulling that piece of string?
Because I'd look silly pushing it.

What goes ha ha plonk?
A man laughing his head off.

My teacher does bird impressions.
Really?
Yes, she watches me like a hawk.

Do you believe in free speech?
Yes.
Good, can I use your phone?

Why does the Prince of Wales wear red, white and blue braces?
To hold his trousers up.

Customer: I want a piece of bacon, and make it lean.
Butcher: Certainly, sir, which way?

What do you get if a cat swallows a ball of wool?
Mittens.

Why do giraffes have such small appetites?
Because with them a little goes a long way.

Have you heard about the man who stole a calendar?
He got 12 months.

Man: I'd like a dog licence, please.
Post Office clerk: Certainly sir, what name?
Man: Rover.

What do you get if you dial 600 4962-4109098?
A blister on your finger.

What kinds of animals can jump higher than a house?
All kinds, houses can't jump.

What's the difference between an Indian and an African elephant?
About 3000 miles.

How can you tell if there's been an elephant in your fridge?
There'll be footprints in the butter.

What's chocolate on the outside, peanut inside, and sings hymns?
A Sunday School Treet.

That's a nice bulldog you've got there.
He isn't a bulldog, he ran into a wall.

Barber: Did you have a red scarf when you came in?
Customer: No.
Barber: Oh dear, I've cut your throat.

My cat plays chess with me.
It must be very intelligent.
Not really, I've won two games so far.

Stall-owner: Want to buy a genuine skull of King Solomon?
Tourist: No thanks, it's much too expensive.
Stall-holder: How about this one? It's cheaper because it's smaller — it's the skull of King Solomon as a child.

How long will the next bus be?
About 20 feet.

My friend eats small pieces of metal every day.
He calls it his staple diet.

A woman walked into a pet shop and asked for
400 beetles, 27 rats, and 3 mice. 'What do you
want them for?' asked the pet shop owner. 'My
landlord's given me notice to quit,' said the
woman, 'and he says I've got to leave the place
just as I found it.'

Two flies were playing football in a saucer. Said
one, 'We'll have to play better than we are at the
moment, we're playing in the cup next week.'

An actor was offered £4000 a week to act in a new film. 'That's good money,' he said, 'what's the film?' 'Treasure Island,' said the producer. 'We want you to play Long John Silver. Be on the set first thing Tuesday morning.' 'For that money I don't mind starting on Monday,' said the actor. 'Not Monday,' said the producer, 'Monday you're having your leg off.'

Teacher: Give me a sentence with the word 'centimetre' in it.
Child: My aunt was coming to stay with us, and I was centimetre.

Joe was on trial for robbery. When the jury announced a verdict of 'Not Guilty' he was delighted, and asked the judge, 'Does that mean I can keep the money?'

What lies at the bottom of the sea and shivers?
A nervous wreck.

What's that you're making?
It's a portable.
A portable what?
I don't know, I've only made the handle.

A man stuck a gun into the pilot's back and demanded, 'Take me to London.' 'But we're going to London,' said the pilot. 'I know,' said the man, 'but I've been hijacked to Egypt twice and I'm taking no chances.'

A flea was riding on a snail when he was overtaken by a flea on a slug. 'What happened to your snail?' asked the first flea. 'I changed it for a convertible,' said the second flea.

Is that new scarecrow of yours any good?
I'll say! It's given the crows such a scare they've brought back the seeds they stole last week.

Have you any dogs going cheap?
Sorry, sir, all dogs go woof woof.

Worried lady to pilot: You will bring me down safely, won't you?
Pilot: Don't worry, madam, I've never left anybody up here yet.

If I had ten oranges in one hand and ten oranges in the other hand, what would I have?
Very big hands.

What do you call a nine-foot canary?
Sir.

Mummy, there's a postman at the door with a parcel marked COD.
Tell him to take it back, I ordered haddock.

My Dad's got a wooden leg.
So what, my Granny's got a wooden chest.

Why did the apple turnover?
Because it saw the jam roll.

Who is always being let down by his mates?
A deep-sea diver.

Why do bees hum?
Because they don't know the words.

KNOCK KNOCK...

Knock knock.
Who's there?
You.
You who?
Did you call me?

Knock knock.
Who's there?
Chilly.
Chilly who?
Chilly me, I've forgotten.

Knock knock
Who's there?
Granny.
Knock knock
Who's there?
Granny.
Knock knock
Who's there?
Granny.
Knock knock
Who's there?
Aunt.
Aunt who?
Aunt you glad I got rid of all those grannies?

Knock knock?
Who's there?
Cook.
Cook who?
That's the first one I've heard this year.

Knock knock.
Who's there?
Amy.
Amy who?
Amy afraid I've forgotten.

Knock knock.
Who's there?
Iris.
Iris who?
Iris you in the name of the law.

An Arab was riding through the Sahara Desert on his camel when he met a man in a skin-diving outfit: flippers, mask, oxygen cylinders, the lot. 'Pardon me,' said the man, 'How far is the sea?' 'About 700 miles,' said the Arab. 'In that case,' said the man, 'I'll wait till the tide comes in.'

Dad, a man called while you were out.
Did he have a bill?
No, just an ordinary nose like everybody else.

Joe: What do you mean by telling everyone I'm an idiot?
Mary: I'm sorry, I didn't know it was supposed to be a secret.

Why do we go to bed?
Because the bed won't come to us.

When it's raining owls don't go out romancing, they just sit in their trees and call out, 'Too wet to woo, too wet to woo.'

A policeman stopped a man who was walking along with a penguin and ordered him to take it to the zoo at once. The next day the policeman saw the same man still with the penguin. 'I told you to take it to the zoo,' he said. 'I did,' said the man, 'now I'm taking him to the pictures.'

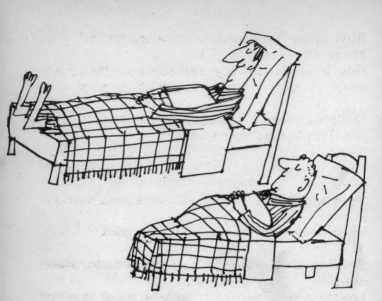

Why are tall people lazy?
Because they lie longer in bed.

Fred was so stupid that when he went to a mindreader, he gave him his money back.

Fred: I've lost my dog.
Bert: Why don't you put an advert in the paper?
Fred: Don't be silly, my dog can't read.

What is the longest night of the year?
A fortnight.

Teacher: Where did King John sign the Magna Carta?
Child: At the bottom.

Boy: Mum, am I made of sage and onion?
Mum: Of course not. Why?
Boy: Because a big boy from the top of the street said he's going to knock the stuffing out of me.

Dad: No, John, you can't play with the hammer, you'll hurt your fingers.
John: No I won't, my friend is going to hold the nails for me.

Teacher: Smith, you should have been in class at nine o'clock!
Smith: Why, did I miss anything good?

Driving instructor: I think you'd better slow down.
Learner: But I'm allowed to do 30 miles an hour in this area.
Driving instructor: But not on the pavement.

Who are you?
I'm the piano tuner, madam.
But I didn't send for you.
No, but your neighbours did.

Sally was saying her bedtime prayers. 'Please, God,' she was saying, 'make New York the capital of America, make New York the capital of America. . . .' Her mother overheard her and said, 'Sally, why do you want God to make New York the capital of America?'
'Because that's what I put in my Geography exam.'

Where would you find a prehistoric cow?
In a moo-seum.

What did the policeman say to the man with three heads?
Hello, hello, hello.

What do you call a sleeping bull?
A bulldozer.

What's the difference between a nail and a bad boxer?
One is knocked in and the other is knocked out.

What should you do if you split your sides laughing?
Run fast until you get a stitch in them.

Mary: Mum, can I have 15p for an old man crying outside in the street?
Mum: Certainly. What's he crying about?
Mary: Toffee apples – 15p each.

What does an elephant do when it rains?
Gets wet.

What sort of car has your family got?
I can't remember its name, I think it starts with T.
Really? Ours starts with petrol.

Why are cooks cruel?
Because they beat eggs,
whip cream and batter
fish.

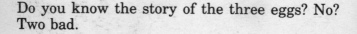

Do you know the story of the three eggs? No?
Two bad.

What has four legs and one foot?
A bed.

What's hairy and coughs?
A coconut with a cold.

Customer: Have you got one-inch nails?
Ironmonger: Yes, sir.
Customer: Then scratch my back, it's itching
something terrible.

The big game hunter heard a scream from his friend: 'A lion has bitten off my foot!'
'Which one?' asked the big game hunter.
'How should I know,' said his friend, 'all these lions look alike to me.'

There was once a tiger who caught measles. He became so spotty he was sent to a leopard colony.

I didn't come here to be made fun of.
Oh, where do you normally go?

Do you have a village idiot?
No, we take it in turns.

There was once a very mean man. He fired a gun outside his door on Christmas Eve, then told his children Santa Claus had shot himself.

I've borrowed my neighbour's bagpipes.
But you can't play the bagpipes.
Neither can he while I've got them.

Why is the bride unlucky?
Because she doesn't marry the best man.

What time is it when an elephant sits on your fence?
Time to get a new one.

Barber: Have you been here before?
Customer: Yes, once.
Barber: Funny, I don't remember your face.
Customer: No, it's healed up since then.

Two boys were paddling in the sea. 'Your feet are really dirty,' said one.
'Yes,' said the other, 'We didn't come here last year.'

Boy: Dad, can I have a glass of water?
Dad: That'll be your tenth glass!
Boy: I know, my room's on fire.

How does a lolly get to school?
On an icecycle.

What runs round a field but doesn't move?
A hedge.

Do you write with your right hand or your left hand?
Well, usually I use a pencil.

My gran is 80 years old and hasn't one grey hair on her head. She's bald.

What would you have if all the cars in England were pink?
A pink carnation.

Man (to little boy): Why are you eating that brick?
Little boy: To build myself up.

My cousin does bird impressions. He eats worms.

There were two eggs in a saucepan, and one said, 'Cor, isn't it hot in here!' And the other one said, 'You wait till you get out, you'll get your head bashed in.'

Sally: Are you going to my party?
Jane: No, I ain't going.
Sally: Now you know what our teacher told us. Not 'aint'. It's, 'I am not going, he is not going, she is not going, they are not going.'
Jane: Blimey nobody ain't going.

Which animals need oiling?
Mice, because they squeak.

A shipboard conjurer used to do incredible tricks every night, but the ship's parrot always used to shout, 'I know how it's done.' One night the ship hit an iceberg and sank, but the conjurer and the parrot managed to grab a life raft and get clear. After three days at sea the parrot finally turned to the conjurer and said, 'All right, I give up. How did you do it?'

WAITER...!

Waiter, there's a dead fly in this soup.
Yes, sir, it's the heat that kills them.

Waiter, how did this fly get in my soup?
It flew, sir.

Waiter, there's a fly in my soup.
Don't worry, sir, there's a spider on the bread.

Waiter, there's a twig in my soup.
Yes, sir, we have branches everywhere.

Waiter, do you ever have a clean tablecloth?
I don't know, sir, I've only been here a year.

Waiter, there's a dead fly in my soup.
What do you expect for 10p, a live one?

Waiter, there's a fly in my soup.
That's all right, sir, he won't drink much.

Waiter, there's a fly in my soup.
Don't make a fuss, sir, they'll all want one.

Waiter, what's this?
It's bean soup, sir.
I know what it's been. What is it now?

Waiter, this coffee tastes like mud.
Well it was ground only five minutes ago.

Waiter, what's this fly doing in my soup?
Looks like the breast-stroke, sir.

Waiter, what's this in my soup?
Don't know, sir, all these insects look the same to me.

Waiter, there's a dead beetle in my soup.
Yes, sir, they're not very good swimmers.

Waiter, there's a hair in this honey.
It must have come from the comb, sir.

Waiter, this coffee tastes like cocoa.
I'm sorry, sir, I've given you tea.

Waiter, your tie is in my soup.
That's all right, sir, it doesn't shrink.

Waiter, there's no chicken in this chicken pie.
So what, sir, you don't get dog in a dog biscuit.

Waiter, could I have some greasy chips, cold beans, and sausages coated in cold fat?
I'm sorry, sir, we couldn't possibly do that.
Why not? You did yesterday.

Waiter, this plate is damp.
Yes, sir, that's the soup.

Waiter, this egg is bad.
Don't blame me, I only lay the table.

Waiter, do the band play requests?
Yes, sir.
Then tell them to play cards till I've finished my dinner.

Waiter, bring me coffee without milk.
We haven't any milk, sir. How about coffee without cream?

Waiter, how long will my sausages be?
About four inches, sir.

Waiter, bring me a glass of milk and a piece of fish.
Fillet.
Yes, right to the top.

Waiter, there's a spider in my soup, send me the manager.
That's no good, he's frightened of them as well.

Waiter, have you got frog's legs?
Yes, sir.
Then hop along and get me a sandwich.

Waiter, have you got frog's legs?
No, sir, I always walk like this.

Worried passenger: Do your planes crash often?
Pilot: No, just once.

Old lady: Where are going to, my little man?
Boy: I'm going to the football match.
Old lady: Oh, which team do you support?
Boy: Crystal Palace.
Old lady: And is it very exciting for you when they win?
Boy: I don't know, I've only been going for two seasons.

This match won't light.
Funny, it did this morning.

Man in the chemist's shop: I'd like some soap please.
Chemist: Certainly, sir. Scented?
Man: No, I'll take it with me.

It was two o'clock in the morning when Fred phoned Joe. The phone rang for hours before it was picked up and Joe's sleepy voice said, 'Hello?' 'Sorry to get you out of bed at this time of night,' said Fred. 'That's all right,' said Joe, 'I had to get up anyway to answer the blasted phone.'

Angry customer: These trousers are too tight. I can't sit down in them.
Tailor: But you asked for them to be skin tight.
Customer: True, but I can sit down in my skin. I can't sit down in these trousers.

What gets wetter as it dries?
A towel.

Commissionaire, call me a taxi.
Right, sir. You're a taxi.

Little Mary was on a train with her mother when suddenly she started to whisper in her mother's ear. 'Mary,' said her mother sharply, 'how many times have I told you it's rude to whisper. If you've got anything to say, say it out loud.' 'All right,' said Mary, 'why has that man got such big ears?'

What's the difference between a buffalo and a bison?
Try washing your hands in a buffalo.

Witness: This woman offered me this dud £1 note, your honour.
Judge: Counterfeit?
Witness: Yes, your honour, she had two.

Who gets the sack as soon as he starts work?
A postman.

What do you call a sailor with eight children?
Daddy.

A racehorse owner was telling off the jockey who had just ridden his horse last in a race. 'You could have gone faster than that!' he yelled. 'Of course I could,' said the jockey, 'but I had to stay with the horse.'

Teacher: You're late again!
Child: Yes, I overslept.
Teacher: You mean you sleep at home as well?

How do you make a cigarette lighter?
Take the tobacco out.

Why has a milk stool got three legs?
Because the cow's got the udder.

Dolphins are so intelligent that within weeks of
being in captivity they can train a man to stand
on the edge of their pool and throw them fish four
times a day.

What goes 99-clop, 99-clop?
A centipede with a wooden leg.

Why is it crazy to break into a bank?
Because it's full of coppers.

What do you get if you cross a shark with a
snowman?
Frostbite.

What is brown, sticky, and shocking?
Electric treacle.

My dog can say his own name.
That's remarkable! What's he called?
Wuff.

Where do you find baby soldiers?
In the infantry.

How do boats cut through waves?
With a sea-saw.

What do you call two rows of cabbages?
A dual cabbageway.

What's the difference between an elephant and a
pillar-box? You don't know? Then it wouldn't be
much good sending you to post a letter.

For two years an old lady's parrot hadn't said anything, and she finally accepted that it was unable to talk. One day, however, as she was feeding it a piece of apple it squawked out, 'There's a maggot in it!' 'You can talk,' cried the old lady, 'why haven't you spoken before?' 'Because up till now the food's been excellent,' said the parrot.

What eight-letter word has only one letter in it? *Envelope*.

Dentist: I'll have to charge you £5 for pulling out that tooth.
Patient: But you told me it would only be £1!
Dentist: Yes, but you yelled so loudly you scared away four other patients.

Why does an ostrich have such a long neck? *Because its head is so far from its body*.

Angry customer: That parrot you sold me won't say a word, and you promised it would repeat everything it heard!
Pet shop owner: So it will, sir, only it's stone deaf.

What's red with green leaves and travels at 100 miles per hour?
An E-type carrot.

What did your Dad say when you broke his golf club?
Shall I leave out the swear words?
Of course.
In that case he didn't say a word.

Teacher: This essay on 'My Dog' is exactly word for word the same as your brother's.
Child: Well, it's the same dog.

Did the butcher have pigs' feet, Sandra?
I couldn't see, Mum, he had his shoes on.

Two birds were sitting on a tree not far from an airport. Suddenly a jet plane roared through the sky close by them. 'Cor, look at that!' said one. 'I bet you'd go fast if your tail was on fire,' said the other.

A man thought he had swallowed a horse and nothing his doctor could say would make him change his mind. Finally the doctor gave him an anaesthetic to put him into a deep sleep. When he woke up, the doctor was standing beside his bed holding a beautiful black stallion by the bridle. 'Nothing more to worry about,' he said, 'we operated on you and took him out.'

'Who are you trying to kid,' said the man, 'the one I swallowed was a grey mare.'

Vicar: If you found a £1 note, would you keep it?
Small boy: No, vicar.
Vicar: That's a good boy. What would you do with it?
Small boy: I'd spend it.

Do you notice any change in me?
No. Why?
I've just swallowed a penny.

Why do polar bears have fur coats?
They'd look odd in tweed ones.

A man lost his ear in an accident at work and asked his friend to help him look for it. After a while, his friend found an ear. 'That's not mine,' said the man, 'mine had a pencil behind it.'

I'd like some rat poison, please.
Have you tried Boots?
I want to poison them, not to kick them to death.

What's yellow and dangerous?
Shark-infested custard.

How do you send chains through the post?
By chain mail.

Would you like a light meal? Eat a candle.

How do you start a Teddy race?
Ready, Teddy, go.

The cafe was well known for its chips. They were in every plate, cup and saucer.

There was once a lazy bank robber.
He phoned up a bank and said, 'This is a hold up, send me £50,000.'

KNOCK KNOCK...

Knock knock.
Who's there?
Lettice.
Lettice who?
Lettice in, it's cold out here.

Will you remember me in a week?
Yes.
Will you remember me in a month?
Yes I will.
Will you remember me in a year?
Yes of course I will!
Knock knock.
Who's there?
See, you've forgotten me already!

Knock knock.
Who's there?
Amos.
Amos who?
A mosquito.

Knock knock.
Who's there?
Ann.
Ann who?
Another mosquito.

Knock knock.
Who's there?
Ivor.
Ivor who?
Ivor you let me in the door or I'll climb in through the window.

Knock knock.
Who's there?
Ya.
Ya who?
I never knew you were a cowboy.

Knock knock.
Who's there?
Gestapo.
Gestapo who?
Ve ask der questions!

Knock knock.
Who's there?
Felix.
Felix who?
Felix my lolly again I'll lick him.

'Give me a kiss,' said the worm.
'Don't be silly, I'm your other end.'

Alsation dog for sale. Eats anything. Very fond of children.

Dad, there's a man at the door with a beard.
Tell him I've already got one.

What swings across a sweet shop going Aaaah-aaaaaah?
Tarzipan.

What do you stuff a parrot with?
Pollyfilla.

A return ticket, please.
Where to?
Back here.

Fred: I don't know whether to be a poet or a painter.
Joe: A poet!
Fred: Oh, you've read one of my poems?
Joe: No, I've seen one of your paintings.

What's the difference between a jeweller and a convict?
One sells watches and the other watches cells.

Air stewardess: I'm sorry, you can't bring that dog with you on the plane.
Passenger: Why not, he's a Skye terrier.

Why did the chicken cross the road?
For some fowl reason.

There was an accident on the motorway today between a police van and a cement mixer in which the prisoners in the police van got away. Police are looking for eight hardened criminals.

I don't want to go to school, Mum. The teachers hate me, and so do the children.
But you've got to go, son, you're the headmaster.

Have you caught anything yet?
When I've caught another it will be one.

My brother's been practising the violin for ten years.
Is he any good at it?
No. He'd been practising for nine years before he found out he wasn't supposed to blow it.

Judge: Have you got a solicitor to represent you?
Prisoner: No, m'lud, I decided to tell the truth.

A small, thin man walked into a pub and shouted angrily, 'Who painted my car bright purple?' A huge man with big muscles got up and said menacingly, 'I did.' 'Oh,' said the small man, 'I thought I'd let you know that the first coat's dry.'

Boy: I've come to collect the reward for returning your canary.
Woman: But that's not a canary – it's a cat.
Boy: I know, the canary's inside it.

What happens to ducks who fly upside down?
They quack up.

What did the hat say to the scarf?
You hang around here, I'll go on ahead.

73

How did Noah manage in the dark?
He turned on the floodlights.

What can fall on water without getting wet?
A shadow.

What do you get if you cross the Atlantic with the Titanic?
Halfway.

Why do leopards never escape from zoos?
Because they're always spotted.

Doctor: Well, I've given you a check-up and I think you're suffering from lack of exercise. Take a brisk walk every morning of not less than two miles.
Patient: I can't do that or I'll get giddy.
Doctor: Why?
Patient: I'm a light-house keeper.

What's the difference between electricity and lightning?
You don't have to pay for lightning.

What is the biggest ant?
An elephant.

What is wrapped in greaseproof paper and hangs around a French cathedral?
The Lunchpack of Notre Dame.

What do you call a rabbit with a lot of money?
A million hare.

What did you get for your birthday?
I got a trumpet, and it's the best present I ever got.
Why?
My Dad gives me 50p a week not to blow it.

Mum: Sally, I've told you it's rude to keep reaching over the table for cakes. Haven't you got a tongue in your head?
Sally: Yes, but my arm's longer.

Mum: John, there were two cream cakes in the larder yesterday, and now there's only one. Why?
John: It must have been so dark I didn't see the other one.

Why don't elephants ride bikes?
Because they haven't got thumbs to ring the bell with.

Dad: Did you have any problems with the exam questions?
Daughter: No, it was the answers I got stuck on.

What's brown and can see just as well from either end?
A cow with its eyes shut.

Here is a warning for motorists: Watch out for small pieces of granite being spread on the roads. And that is the end of the chipping forecast.

A carpenter was laying a carpet for a lady, and he saw a bump in the carpet, so he hit it with his hammer. A few moments later the lady came in and said, 'Have you seen my baby hamster?'

What's got eight legs, is green and yellow, with blue spots?
I don't know, what has?
Nor do I, but there's one on your collar.

A Martian spaceship landed in an empty petrol station, and the leading Martian went straight up to a petrol pump and said, 'Take me to your leader!' There was no answer. 'Oi,' said the Martian, 'take your finger out of your ear when I'm talking to you.'

There was a man who had jelly in one ear and custard in the other. He was a trifle deaf.

Why don't elephants eat penguins?
They can't get the wrapping paper off.

Old lady: Could you see me across the road?
Boy scout: I don't know, madam, I'll go over there and have a look.

Tourist guide: That brass plaque on the deck is where Sir Francis Drake fell.
Tourist: I'm not surprised, I nearly tripped over it myself.

Pilot: Attention all passengers. If you look out at the port engine you will see it is on fire. And if you look out at the starboard engine you will see that it has stopped working. And if you look out and down you will see a small inflatable raft in the water . . . and that is where I am speaking to you from.

Is it true that an apple a day keeps the doctor away?
Yes.
Well, give me an apple quick, I've just broken the doctor's window.

What would happen if pigs could fly?
Bacon would go up.

Dad, the boy next door said I look just like you.
Really? And what did you say?
Nothing, he's bigger than me.

Mum: If you've finished your meal, Sarah, you can say grace.
Sarah: All right. Thanks for the meal, Lord.
Mum: That wasn't much of a grace.
Sarah: It wasn't much of a meal.

Why do you call your dog Buttons?
He's often attached to trousers.

Museum attendant: That vase you've just broken was 2000 years old!
Small boy: Thank goodness, I thought it was new.

What's your new dog's name?
I don't know, he won't tell me.

A man walked into a police station and put a dead rat on the counter. 'Somebody threw this in my front window,' he complained. 'Right, sir,' said the police sergeant, 'if you come back in six months and no one's claimed it you can keep it.'

KNOCK KNOCK...

Knock knock.
Who's there?
Luke.
Luke who?
Luke through the keyhole and you'll see.

Knock knock.
Who's there?
Wood.
Wood who?
Would you believe I forgot the joke?

Knock knock.
Who's there?
Eileen.
Eileen who?
Eileen on doors.

Knock knock.
Who's there?
Ach.
Ach who?
Sorry, I didn't know you had a cold.

Knock knock.
Who's there?
A little man.
A little man who?
A little man who can't reach the doorbell.

Knock knock.
Who's there?
Ken.
Ken who.
Ken I come in?

Knock knock.
Who's there?
A little old lady.
A little old lady who?
I didn't know you could yodel.

Knock knock.
Who's there?
Ivan.
Ivan who?
Ivan an idea you don't want to let me in.

Knock knock.
Who's there?
Isabel.
Isabel who?
Isabel really necessary
on a bike?

What did the astronaut see in his frying pan?
An unidentified frying object.

This new hearing aid I've got is so small that nobody notices it. It's wonderful.
That's great. How much did it cost?
Half past two.

Dad, what would happen if I stole that budgerigar?
You'd go to prison.
Oh, you wouldn't forget to feed him while I was away, would you?

Where do parrots go to study?
A polly technic.

Excuse me, sir, your dog's been chasing a man on a bicycle.

Ridiculous, constable, my dog can't ride a bicycle.

Who led 10,000 pigs up a hill and then back down again?

The Grand Old Duke of Pork.

Why is the level crossing gate half open?

Well, we're half expecting a train.

What do you get when you cross an elephant with a mouse?

Big holes in the skirting board.

First cat: How did you do in the milk-drinking contest?

Second cat: I won by four laps.

I've lost my canary. What shall I do?
Call for the Flying Squad.

Have you ever seen a man-eating tiger?
No, but I once saw a man eating chicken.

Boy: How much are these marbles?
Shopkeeper: 5p for two. 4p for one.
Boy: Here's a penny, I'll have the other one.

Dad: What did you learn in school today?
Son: I learned that those sums you did for me
were wrong.

I've just finished painting your portrait. Don't
you think it looks just like you?
*Er ... er ... it probably looks better from a
distance.*
See, I told you it was just like you.

Who didn't invent the aeroplane?
The Wrong Brothers.

There were ten cats in a boat. One jumped out,
how many were left?
None. All the others were copycats.

What happens if you throw a stone into the Red
Sea?
It gets wet.

What is an elephant's favourite game in a car?
Squash.

Will you bounce up and down on your bed please,
sir.
Why, nurse?
I forgot to shake the bottle before giving you
your medicine.

Two escaped lions walked along the beach at Brighton, and one said to the other, 'Not much of a crowd for a bank holiday.'

Teacher: I said you were to draw a house and a man. Where's the man?
Child: In the house.

This parrot is very clever. If you pull his right leg he sings, and if you pull his left leg, he whistles. And what happens if you pull both legs?
'I fall off my perch,' said the parrot.

Teacher: What is the outside of a tree called?
Girl: I don't know.
Teacher: Bark, girl.
Girl: Woof woof.

A violinist was standing in the jungle playing so beautifully that one by one all the animals came out of the jungle and sat down to listen to him, until a lion came out of the trees, and went up to the violinist and ate him with one gulp. 'Why did you do that?' asked a tiger, 'He was playing such beautiful music.' The lion cupped its hand to its ear and said, 'What?'

Two snakes were in the zoo, and one said to the other, 'Are we poisonous?' 'Why?' asked the other snake. 'Because I've just bitten my lip,' said the first snake.

Mum: I've made the chicken soup.
Boy: Thank heavens for that, I thought it was for us!

My Mum and Dad were in the iron and steel business.
She ironed and he stole.

Dentist: Stop pulling such faces and waving your arms about, I haven't touched your tooth yet.

Boy: I know, but you're standing on my foot.

A woman with a baby in her arms was sitting in a railway station waiting-room crying. A porter came up to her and asked what the trouble was. 'Some people were in here just now and they were so rude about my son,' she cried. 'They all said he was ugly.'

'There, there, don't cry,' said the porter kindly. 'Shall I get you a cup of tea?'

'Oh that would be nice,' said the woman, wiping her eyes, 'you are very kind.'

'That's all right,' said the porter, 'and while I'm at it I'll get a banana for your monkey.'

DOCTOR, DOCTOR!

Doctor: Do you have trouble making up your mind?
Patient: Well, yes and no. . . .

Doctor doctor, I feel like a £1 note.
Well, go shopping, the change will do you good.

Doctor doctor, I have 59 seconds to live!
Wait a minute.

Doctor, will you help me out?
Certainly, which way did you come in?

Doctor, I keep stealing chairs.
Take a seat.

Doctor, I think I'm a yoyo.
Sit down sit down sit down sit down. . . .

Doctor, I think I'm a watch.
Don't worry, just sit down and unwind.

Doctor, I feel like a pack of cards.
I'll deal with you later.

Doctor, I feel like a pair of curtains.
Pull yourself together.

Doctor, what can I do for a splinter in my finger?
Rub it on a piece of rough wood.

Doctor, I keep thinking there are two of me.
Could you repeat that, and this time please don't both speak at once.

Doctor, my hair keeps falling out. What can you give me to keep it in?
Try this cardboard box.

Doctor, I can't sleep.
Lie on the edge of the bed, you'll soon drop off.

Doctor, I snore so loudly I keep myself awake, what can I do?
Sleep in another room.

Doctor, I think I'm a bird.
Just perch yourself there and I'll tweet you in a minute.

Doctor, I'm only two feet tall.
You'll just have to be a little patient.

Doctor, I've lost my memory.
When did this happen?
When did what happen?

Patient: Doctor, I've got an awful pain in my left leg.
Doctor: It's just old age.
Patient: But I've had my right leg just as long and that doesn't hurt.

Woman: Doctor, I'm worried about my husband. For six months he's been thinking he's a chicken.
Doctor: Good grief, why didn't you come and see me earlier?
Woman: I would have but we needed the eggs.

Doctor, will my measles be better next week?
I don't make rash statements.

Will this medicine cure me, doctor?
Well, no one's ever come back after taking it.

Doctor: What seems to be the trouble?
Patient: I keep thinking that when I speak no one can hear me.
Doctor: What seems to be the trouble?

Doctor: Did you drink your orange juice after your bath?
Patient: No, after drinking the bath I didn't have much room for the orange juice.

Doctor: Your body's getting fat, you'll have to diet.
Patient: Right, doctor. What colour?

With special thanks to all those children who contributed:

Lydia Aarons
Chefoor Ahmed
Debra Ainge
Ann Ainsworth
Shabu Ali
Sohbat Ali
Sundar Ali
Clare Allmond
Ruhul Amin
Jeremy Arnold
Steven Ashley
Mohammed Atique
Antony Attwood
Nissar Awan

A. Bains
Sabina Baltierrez
Asya Begum
Rezina Begum
Mark Bierton
Montrose Bill
Sunit Biswas
Janet Borrowdale
Christine Botting
M. Lisa Bowen
Stewart Bowman
Colin Boyd
Garry Boyle
John Bradshaw
Juliet Branford
Jill Broome
Mandy Brook
Stuart Brooks
Clare Brown
Lisa J. Byfield

Stephen Camings
Erika Carroll
Heidi Carroll
Lucy Castle
Andrew Chamberlain
Kiran Chauhan
Sunil Cheekory

Meenu Chopra
Tarique-ul-Hassan
 Chowdhury
Olha Ciniawskyj
Amanda Claridge
Martin Clark
Allison Cleary
Audrey Coleman
Andrew Crane

Melanie Davis
G. Peter Dawson
Richard Dean
Michelle Deddy
Brian Delaney
Alan Dennis
Kenneth Devine
Martin Dew
Jasprit Dhaliwal
Suckhijeet Dhaliwal
Samuel Dill
Lisa Dix
Jane Dunn

Mandy Edmonds
Duncan Eldridge
Sharon Elksnis
Paul Elksnis
Christina Evans
Philip Eyers

Sarah Jane Fagence
Nicola Fairey
Ruth Fairman
Iain Flitton
Natalie Foster
Suzanne France
Sonia Frezza
Mary Froggatt
Joanne Frost

Tina Gaziano
Vali Gembali

Nadeem Ghani
Javid Gilani
Wayne Gilbey
Deborah Gilbey
Alison Gilmartin
Jeannette Gomes
Allun Govier
Faye Green
Lynda Griffin
Lee Griggs

John Hand
Lee Hardy
Claire Harris
Peter Harris
Patricia Hart
Tracy Henry
Lucy Hinkley
Patrick Hughes
A. Hussain
Ahktar Hussain
Paul Hutchinson

Anthony Ingram
Helen Ivory

Juliet Jackson
Richard Jenkins
Karn Johal
Bobby Jose
Wayne Judkins

Nighat Kalloo
Shannaz Kalloo
Nasev Kaur
Rabinda Kaur
Sarujeet Kaur
Karen Keeney
Caroline Kelly
Jackie Kendall
Sarah Kenney
Sarah Kern
Shalim Khalik

Raja Khan
Shala Khan
Sultana Khan
Darren King
Neil Kitchener
Davinder Kundi
Naeem Latif
Safeena Latif
Angela Lee
Sally Loeber

Bridie McCandless
Paul McCready
Sharon McGuire
Sharon McLaughlin
William McAvock
Nazma Malik
Jenny Manton
Sarfraz Manzoor
Kathleen Marley
Paul Martin
Grace Mathai
Andrew Mayfield
Stephen Mead
Nilesh Mehta
Kalpna Mehta
Sundip Mehta
Anna Melillo
Adam Mirza
Roisin Mirza
Kate Mitchell
Pauline Morgan
Sharon Muir
Nicola Mulara
John Murray

Lianne Nash
Linda Naughton
Haq Nawaz
Stephen Neufville

Claire O'Connell
Donna Owens

Michael Packwood
Samantha Parker

Shirley Parry
Iftkhar Parvaz
Rajesh Patel
Adele Paterson
Sarah Paterson
Vilash Pattni
Migel Pidgeon
Robert Pinnock
Gail Porter
Paula Priestley
Tracey Priestley
Keith Pyett
Sarah Pyper

Sally Quinn

Lina Raffermati
Margaret Raffermati
Alison Randall
Shahin Rashid
Tracey Ratcliffe
Timothy Reason
Jason John Reynolds
Helen Rice
Julie Roberts
Saroj Rom
Alan Ross
Paul Ross
Claire Rowley
Matthew Rutt
Caroline Ryan
Colin Ryan
Joanne Ryan

Antonietta di Salvo
Elena di Salvo
Tiziana di Salvo
Gavin Samsa
Isobel Scott
Alan Selby
Chris Shacklady
Asim Shafi
Anwar Shah
Farhana Azmat Shah
Ghazala Shaheen
Mohini Sharman

Inderjeet Siduh
Andrew Smith
Donna Smith
Kim Smith
Rita Sohal
Angelica Solano
Dipak Songara
Richard Spary
John Spurgeon
Julia Staines
Emma Stanbridge
Mark Stephenson
Amanda Stratton
Salim Suleman

Susan Taylor
Samantha Thompson
Kevin Tidborough
Nigel Timms
Shelley Toomey
A. Trussell
Andrew Tufton
Veronica Tunn

Zanub Lal-Uddin
Shirim Ullah

David Wallenbarn
Stewart Walters
Raymond Walsh
Tracey Ward
Lynn Watson
Aamena Wazir
Catherine West
Graham West
T. West
Steven Whiting
Alex Whittle
Janice Williams
Steven Ward

Nicola Yates
Norman Young

Tabasim Zia